The Test

by
Linda Kita-Bradley

Grass Roots Press

The Test is published by
Grass Roots Press, a division of Literacy Services of Canada Ltd.

www.grassrootsbooks.net

ACKNOWLEDGMENTS

We acknowledge the financial support of the Government of Canada through the Canada Book Fund (CBF) for our publishing activities.

Produced with the assistance of the Government of Alberta, Alberta Multimedia Development Fund.

Government of Alberta ■

Editor: Dr. Pat Campbell
Photography: Grass Roots Press
Book design: Lara Minja, Lime Design Inc.

Library and Archives Canada Cataloguing in Publication

Kita-Bradley, Linda, 1958–
    The test / Linda Kita-Bradley.

ISBN 978–1–926583–89–1

    1. Readers for new literates. I. Title.

PE1126.N43K5875 2012   428.6'2   C2012–902995–5

This is Dan.

Dan is taking a class.

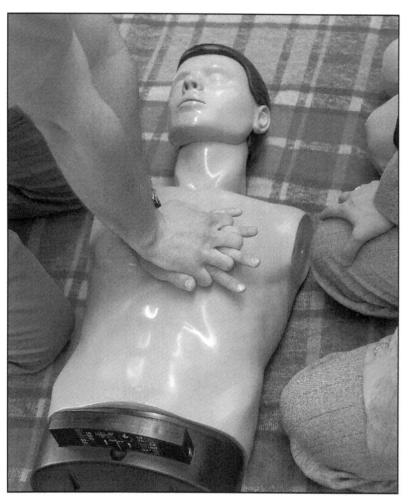

He needs to learn first aid.

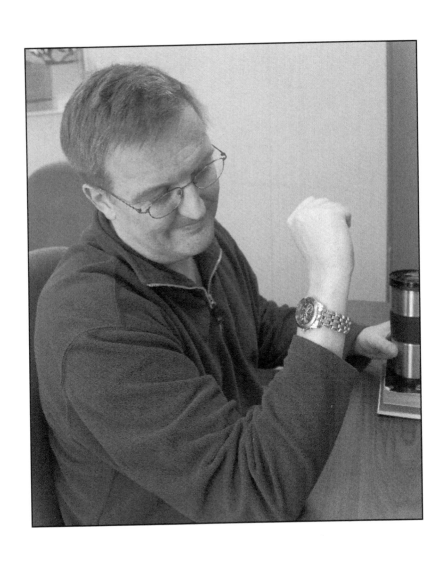

Dan is always on time for class.

He takes notes.

He asks questions.

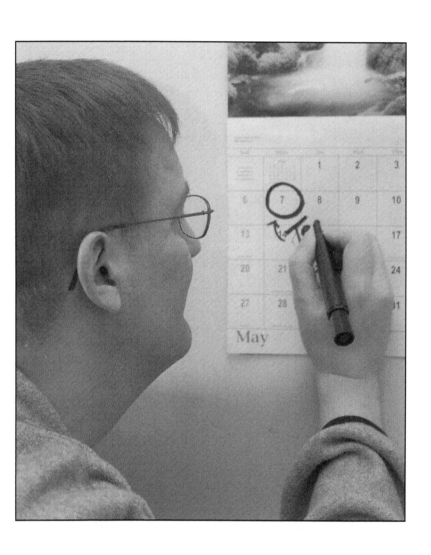

Dan has a test on Monday.

Dan is afraid of tests.

So Dan studies hard.

Dan is ready for the test.

But Dan cannot sleep.

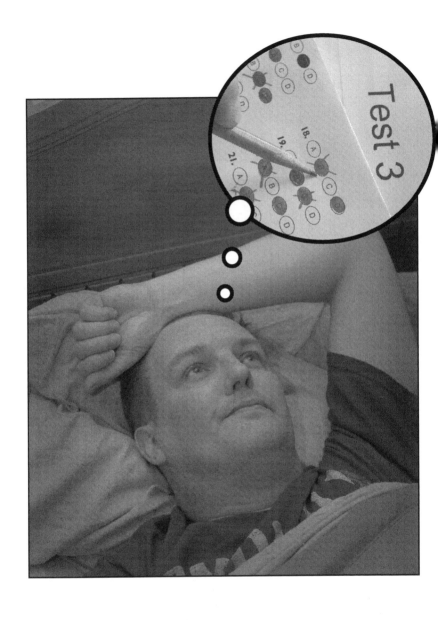

Dan thinks about the test all night.

Dan goes to class.

He starts the test.

He starts to feel hot.

His mind goes blank.

Oh!
Dan can see some answers.

Dan thinks, "Should I copy?"

"I studied so hard.
I need to pass."

Dan copies some answers.

He fills in more answers.

Dan hands in his test.
Now what?

Made in the USA
Las Vegas, NV
25 February 2022

44579279R00015